THE GREAT BIG IRISH ANNUAL 2022

Gill Books

THIS BOOK BELONGS TO

NAME ....

ADDRESS ....

AGE ....

CONTENTS

Welcome to

THE GREAT BIG IRISH ANNUAL 2022!

INSIDE, YOU'LL FIND ...

LOTS OF FUN THINGS TO MAKE AND DO

CRAZY FACTS AND SILLY SCIENCE

HECTIC HISTORY AND SERIOUS SPORTS

... AND MUCH, MUCH MORE.

This is **YOUR BOOK**. You can **DRAW ON IT, SHARE IT, SPILL MILK ON IT** or **USE THE PAGES TO LINE YOUR GERBIL'S CAGE** (well, maybe not).

So jump in!

YOUR BEST BiTS

The year 2021 was a **pretty crazy** time for everyone. How was your year?

MY FAVOURITE PART OF THE YEAR WAS

MY LEAST FAVOURITE PART WAS

THIS YEAR, **I LEARNED**

THIS YEAR, I GREW

THIS YEAR, **I TRIED**

THIS YEAR, **I VISITED**

IN 2022, I WANT TO

HiSTORY BUFFS

2021 FLASH BACK

15 YEARS AGO ...

Pluto was downgraded to a dwarf planet ... poor Pluto!

50 YEARS AGO ...

NASA's Apollo 14 became the third mission to land on the moon – and the first to play golf!

25 YEARS AGO ...

the first Pokémon game was released!

100 YEARS AGO ...

A Danish explorer first set foot on Kaffeklubben Island, the most northerly point of land on Earth.

200 YEARS AGO ...

Mexico declared independence from Spain and the Treaty of Córdoba was signed. ¡Viva México!

¡VIVA MÉXICO!

WHEN A KNIGHT WAS KILLED IN BATTLE, WHAT DID THEY PUT ON HIS GRAVE

RUST IN PEACE.

ANCIENT ART

Around **700 BC**, an advanced culture from Europe started to settle in Ireland. These **Celts were fierce fighters**, but they were also **known for their artwork**. They used **patterns** and **animal shapes** to create beautiful designs.

n you **COLOUR** this one in?

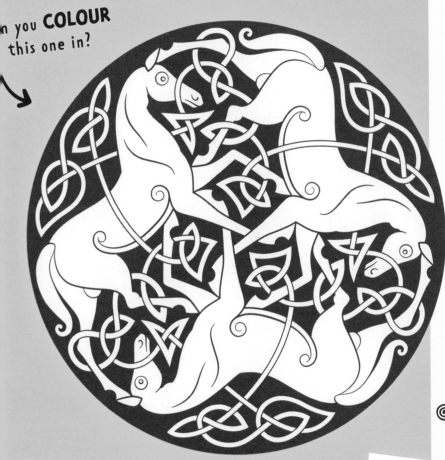

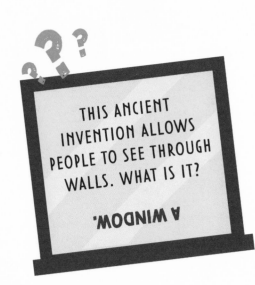

THIS ANCIENT INVENTION ALLOWS PEOPLE TO SEE THROUGH WALLS. WHAT IS IT?

A WINDOW.

SMARTY PANTS!

The most famous example of Celtic art is the *Book of Kells*. Some of the details in this book are so small, they can only be seen with a magnifying glass!

3

JOKES AND RIDDLES

Try out these brainteasers on your friends and watch them scratch their heads!

I HAVE A TAIL AND A HEAD, BUT NO BODY. WHAT AM I?

A coin.

WHAT IRISH ROCK IS AS LIGHT AS A FEATHER?

A shamrock.

I SHAVE EVERY DAY, BUT MY BEARD STAYS THE SAME. WHAT AM I?

A barber.

16 06 68 88 ? 98
WHAT'S THE MISSING NUMBER?

(Hint: turn the book upside down!)

IF A BROTHER, A SISTER AND THEIR DOG WEREN'T UNDER AN UMBRELLA, WHY DIDN'T THEY GET WET?

It wasn't raining.

WHAT'S ALWAYS IN FRONT OF YOU, BUT CANNOT BE SEEN?

The future.

RIDDLE ME THIS!

WHAT KIND OF ANIMAL EATS WITH ITS TAIL?

All kinds of animals – they can't take them off!

WHAT LOSES A HEAD IN THE MORNING, BUT GAINS ONE AT NIGHT?

A pillow.

WHAT STARTS WITH A P, ENDS WITH A T, AND HAS A BAJILLION LETTERS IN IT?

The post.

WHY DOES A SEAGULL ALWAYS FLY OVER THE SEA?

Because if it flew over the bay, it would be a bagel!

A BUS DRIVER GOES THE WRONG WAY DOWN A ONE-WAY STREET, BUT THE GARDAÍ DON'T STOP HIM! WHY?

He was walking.

WHAT TRAVELS ALL AROUND THE WORLD BUT ALWAYS STAYS IN THE CORNER?

A stamp.

A COWBOY RIDES INTO TOWN ON FRIDAY, STAYS FOR THREE DAYS, AND THEN LEAVES ON FRIDAY. HOW DID HE DO IT?

His horse was called Friday.

WHAT IS BLACK WHEN IT'S CLEAN AND WHITE WHEN IT'S DIRTY?

A blackboard.

SCIENCE LAB

Feeling a bit **inventive**? Curious about how the world works? Or do you just feel like making a big mess?

Thanks to the **CORONAVIRUS**, we've all learned about germs and how they can be passed on.

But **HOW** do **GERMS TRANSFER SO EASILY** from one thing to another?

Some people think all scientists are a little bit MAD. Write your own **CRAZY IDEAS** here:

GLITTER HANDS

What you'll need

some baby oil

glitter

a friend

soap

Tip: Make sure your glitter is eco-friendly. Otherwise, when you wash it off, it could get into the ocean and hurt the fish and animals that live there!

1. Rub a little bit of baby oil on your hands. Get your friend to do the same.

2. Now, one person sprinkles some glitter on their hands. These are the 'germs' that are spread by sneezing and coughing.

3. Shake hands with your friend. What happens? What if your friend touches their face or shakes hands with another person?

4. Try washing your glittery hands in cold water without soap. Did the germs go away?

5. Wash your hands again, using warm water and soap this time, for at least 20 seconds.

6. All clean!

PAVEMENT CHALK

Did you know that **EGGSHELLS CONTAIN CALCIUM**, the same thing that is used to make chalk?

If you have egg lovers in your house, you can make your own **ECO-FRIENDLY OUTDOOR CHALK**.

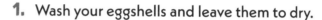

What you'll need

5 eggshells

mortar and pestle

1 tsp plain flour

2 tsp hot water

food dye

kitchen roll

1. Wash your eggshells and leave them to dry.

2. When the eggshells are completely dry, use a mortar and pestle to grind them until you have a very fine powder. This can take a while – if you see a lazy adult around, ask them to help!

3. Put your eggshell powder into a bowl. Add the flour and hot water and mix to make a stiff paste.

4. Now, add some food dye to your eggshell paste. You can split the mix to make two small chalks, or just make one big one.

5. Put your eggshell paste onto some thick kitchen roll or paper towel. Roll it into a tube to mould your chalk into a long thin shape.

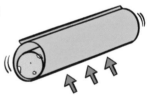

6. Leave the chalk to dry for at least a full day – it needs this time to harden. Once it has completely dried, you can use it outside.

SMARTY PANTS!

The white Cliffs of Dover in England are made of chalk, which was formed by tiny sea creatures being squished together for millions of years. The slow movement of the Earth's crust pushed the chalk upwards to form cliffs.

7

WILD AT HEART
TRUE OR FALSE?

A
Young sunflowers move their petals to track the sun across the sky.
✓ ✗

B
A male badger is called a boydger.
✓ ✗

C
People used to think that the cry of a fox was the scream of a banshee.
✓ ✗

D
The red deer is Ireland's largest land animal.
✓ ✗

E
Sycamore trees have seeds shaped like aeroplanes.
✓ ✗

F
Natterer's bats are found in Ireland.
✓ ✗

G
A group of owls is called a parliament.
✓ ✗

H
There are no reptile native to Ireland.
✓ ✗

I
A squirrel's front teeth never stop growing.
✓ ✗

J
Bees wiggle their bums to pass messages to each other.
✓ ✗

I DON'T BE-LEAF IT!

Can you match these leaves with the tree they come from?
Try to collect one of each and glue them here!

| OAK | HORSE CHESTNUT | IVY | ASH | SYCAMORE | BIRCH |

8

INSECT HOTEL

Insects play an important part in our environment. You can help them by **CREATING A SAFE SPACE** where they can live.

The best time to make your hotel is in autumn, so the insects have somewhere to spend the winter. **YOU WON'T NEED TO INCLUDE A JACUZZI!**

1. Pick a site for your hotel. You can do this in your garden or in a park. It should be a quiet spot with firm ground, and no noisy neighbours!

2. Gather lots of bits and pieces together for your hotel rooms. You can use bricks, planks of wood, dead leaves, straw, grass, pine cones, bamboo and old pots.

3. Start by adding some rocks to the ground floor of your hotel, then wedge them down with a piece of wood. Do this a few more times, making sure your hotel is stable and won't fall over.

4. Now, start filling in the spaces on each floor with stones, grass, leaves and any other natural materials you can find. Try to create lots of openings of different sizes – insects love squeezing into nooks and crannies.

5. When everything is wedged in tightly, add a large piece of wood or some plastic for a roof. Time for the grand opening!

Tip: Some insects like to close the door behind them, so keep an eye out for any blocked-up holes.

WHY ARE FROGS ALWAYS SO HAPPY?

THEY CAN EAT WHATEVER BUGS THEM.

9

ST PATRICK'S DAY

On St Patrick's Day, everyone around the world is a little bit Irish. People throw parties and organise parades. Some cities even dye their rivers green!

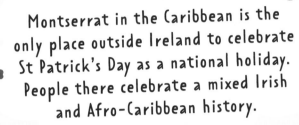

DANCING FEET

These Irish dancers are looking a bit dull. Can you **colour in their clothes** for a St Patrick's Day performance?

DID YOU KNOW?

Montserrat in the Caribbean is the only place outside Ireland to celebrate St Patrick's Day as a national holiday. People there celebrate a mixed Irish and Afro-Caribbean history.

MINTY O'BISCUITS

These minty treats are **EXTRA LUCKY**. When you bake them, something magical will happen ... you'll get to **EAT BISCUITS!**

WHAT YOU'LL NEED

MAKES 12

125g butter, softened
100g dark brown sugar
2 eggs
175g self-raising flour
50g cocoa powder
50g mint chocolate bar, chopped up

1. Preheat the oven to 190°C (or 170°C in a fan oven).

2. Line a tray with baking paper.

3. Beat the butter and sugar in a bowl until light and fluffy, then beat in the eggs one at a time.

4. Add the flour and cocoa powder and beat into the mixture until it forms a stiff paste. Then fold through the chopped chocolate.

5. Place one tablespoon of the mix on the baking paper. Repeat until you run out of dough, making sure to leave room for the mix to spread out.

6. Bake for 12–15 minutes, leave to cool and enjoy!

We all know that a rainbow is made up of SEVEN COLOURS. But how many words can you make out of the letters in

RAINBOW?

HERE'S A FEW TO START YOU OFF:

BORN
WARN
BROW

GAGA FOR GAA

2021 WAS A STRANGE YEAR FOR GAA DUE TO COVID-19, BUT YOU CAN DO THESE ACTIVITIES IN YOUR OWN HOME!

Hurley Burly

Can you spot the **5 differences** between these two exciting shots?

SMARTY PANTS!

In Quebec, Canada, a law was passed in 1845 to ban hurling in the narrow alleyways of the city because it was too dangerous.

HAVE YOU GOT WHAT IT TAKES?

Can you find these words? Score a point for every word you get!

FOOTBALL HURLEY PENALTY

GAELIC ALLSTAR PUCK

REFEREE SLIOTAR COUNTY

HANDBALL CAMOGIE

A	M	L	I	K	D	R	Z	F	P	G	J	K	N	S
F	L	N	L	Y	S	R	M	E	U	C	G	T	U	N
C	L	L	Y	A	P	W	I	X	C	Y	F	Q	I	O
A	A	N	S	T	B	G	M	G	K	E	T	N	H	D
L	B	D	R	T	O	T	D	M	P	L	X	B	F	Y
Z	D	I	F	M	A	P	O	U	P	R	R	K	T	S
E	N	X	A	U	X	R	F	O	R	U	F	L	S	D
J	A	C	M	S	C	Y	O	Y	F	H	A	E	Y	X
U	H	T	B	N	C	G	T	Q	F	N	M	R	L	K
Z	K	O	R	H	L	X	C	N	E	Y	E	B	D	O
G	V	F	A	A	U	U	A	P	U	F	S	R	X	E
C	U	G	L	I	O	C	A	P	E	O	O	Q	U	X
A	K	G	A	E	L	I	C	R	H	D	C	H	O	O
U	L	G	U	D	S	J	E	Y	K	G	A	V	Z	T
G	G	K	A	W	Z	E	Y	R	A	T	O	I	L	S

DESIGN YOUR KIT

Can you design your very own GAA team kit? Make sure to use lots of colours so that you stand out on the pitch.

HERE'S SOME INSPIRATION TO GET YOU STARTED.

ARTIST'S STUDIO

Peter Donnelly is an Irish illustrator and children's author. His books include *The President's Glasses, The President's Cat, The President's Surprise, The Dead Zoo* and *Up On the Mountain.*

CHATTING WITH PETER DONNELLY

Q. DID YOU ALWAYS WANT TO BE AN ILLUSTRATOR?

A. When I was young, I dreamt of being an archaeologist. I was fascinated with very, very old stuff. I wanted to discover something cool like a Viking sword or a Celtic chariot. Imagine that? But I also loved to draw things. I realised I could draw buried swords and chariots and not get my knees dirty, so I became an illustrator instead.

Q. WHAT TIPS DO YOU HAVE FOR YOUNG ARTISTS?

A. Draw or paint what you love in life. Start with things that interest you and you will enjoy drawing. Once you practise, you will get better, and then moving onto more difficult ideas will become a little easier. Art is about discovery and how you like to express yourself. We are all good at art – but the more you do, the better you'll become at it!

Q. HOW DO YOU COME UP WITH IDEAS FOR YOUR BOOKS?

A. Sometimes a simple drawing that I make will inspire an idea for a character. Other times, I'll listen to people chatting, or I'll read an article that I find interesting, and it will give me an idea for a story. *The Dead Zoo* was based on all my visits to the Natural History Museum as a kid.

Q. TELL US A JOKE!

A. I tried to be a self-portrait painter ...

But in the end, it just wasn't me.

COMIC CREATOR

Use the tips from Peter Donnelly to make your own comic strip.

First, you need a starring character:

DINOSAUR SPECIALIST
DIAMOND THIEF
PASTRY CHEF

Then you need a location for the story:

A DARK TUNNEL
UNDERWATER
DESERT ISLAND

Finally, you need a problem for them to face:

SORE TOES
LOST TREASURE
AN ASTEROID

Introduce your character and setting

NOW YOU'RE READY TO START YOUR STORY!

Now, give them a problem to solve

Now, give your story an ending ... to be continued?!

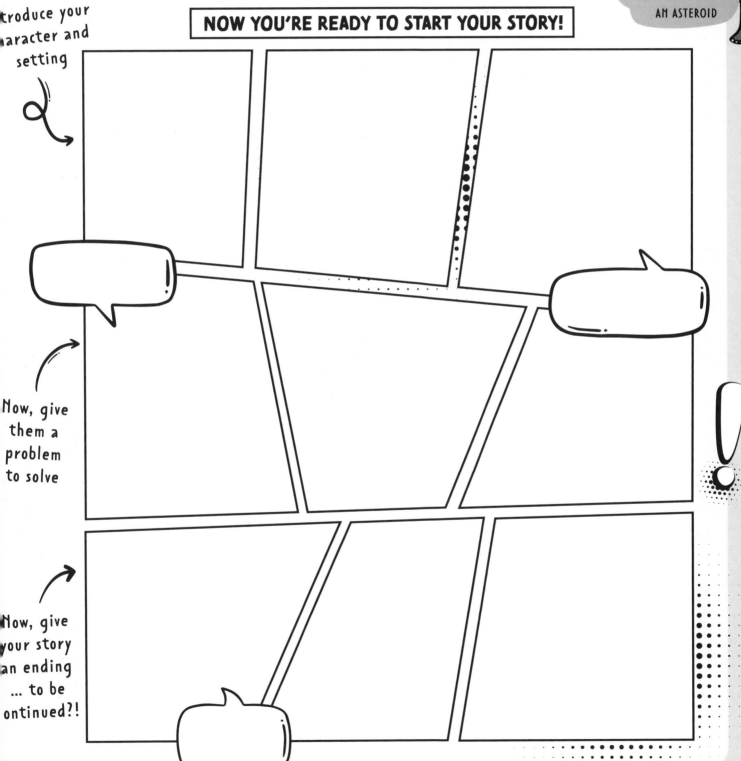

AROUND IRELAND

With this board game, you can travel around the country from your bedroom!

You'll need a **dice** and **a small token** for each player.

At the **GIANT'S CAUSEWAY**, a giant throws you back 3 spaces

Shelter from the rain at **MALIN HEAD** weather station – miss a go

Swim across **LOUGH NEAGH** – float forward 1 space

Take the **BELFAST** train forward 2 spaces

Watch the sunrise at **NEWGRANGE** – miss a go

Find a shortcut through **MARBLE ARCH CAVES** – go forward 2 spaces

In **SLIGO**, grab your board and surf forward 1 space

Slide down **CROAGH PATRICK** – skip

THE DSPCA

Founded in **1840**, the Dublin Society for Prevention of Cruelty to Animals (DSPCA) is **Ireland's oldest and largest animal welfare organisation**.

A team of DSPCA inspectors **respond to thousands of calls** each year, rescuing animals that need their help. The veterinary staff help these animals get well enough to be either **rehomed** or, in the case of wild animals, **released**.

It **rescues**, **rehabilitates** and **rehomes** all kinds of sick, injured and cruelly treated animals, both domestic and wild. It finds homes for over **2,500 animals each year** and reunites many lost animals with their owners.

DSPCA
The Dublin Society for Prevention of Cruelty to Animals

GET THAT GOAT

Can you colour in this **CHEEKY GOAT** waiting for a new home at the DSPCA?

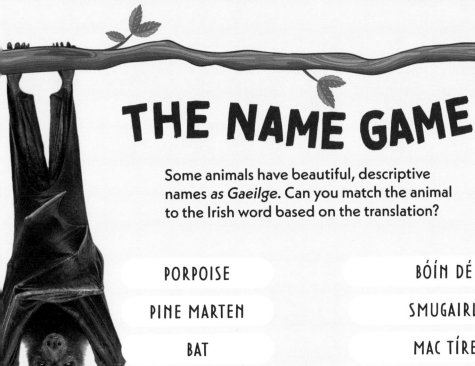

THE NAME GAME

Some animals have beautiful, descriptive names *as Gaeilge*. Can you match the animal to the Irish word based on the translation?

PORPOISE

PINE MARTEN

BAT

DADDY LONGLEGS

JELLYFISH

FOX

WOLF

LADYBIRD

BÓIN DÉ (god's little cow)

SMUGAIRLE RÓIN (seal spit)

MAC TÍRE (son of the land)

MADRA RUA (red dog)

SCIATHÁN LEATHAIR (leather wings)

CAT CRAINN (tree cat)

MUC MHARA (pig of the sea)

SNÁTHAID AN PHÚCA (the devil's needle)

Draw your **FAVOURITE ANIMAL** here. It could be your pet, a wild animal or something completely made-up!

Make sure you fill the bowl with its favourite food.

TECH CORNER

Video games, computers, robots, coding and AI – read all about it in the **TECHNOLOGY TIMES**! But the photographers are on their holidays. Can you fill in for them by drawing pictures to go with these articles?

TECHNOLOGY TIMES

MARS INVASION

In February 2021, NASA's Perseverance rover and the Ingenuity helicopter landed on the surface of Mars. Then, in May 2021, China's Tianwen-1 lander-rover arrived there too. Hope the Martians don't mind their new neighbours ...

GAME OR SHAME?

A 2021 study found that over half of kids would like to see gaming on the school curriculum ... but only a quarter of parents agreed! What do you think?

WOLF VS BEAR

A Japanese town has used robot wolves to scare away bears that have become a nuisance in the countryside. The Monster Wolf has four legs, a shaggy body and red, glowing eyes. When its motion detectors are activated, it moves its head, lights up and howls. Sadly, real wolves went extinct in Japan more than a century ago.

GIMME A HAND?

Want to make your **VERY OWN ROBOT HAND** with **MOVING FINGERS**? Here's how!

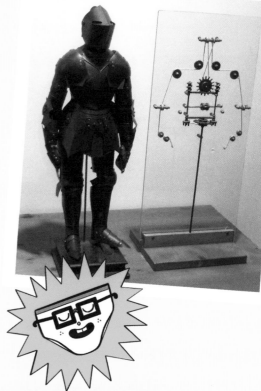

WHAT YOU'LL NEED

pencil
sticky tape
scissors
cardboard
5 straws
wool

1. Trace around your hand on a big piece of cardboard and cut it out. The bigger the hand, the better, so you could use an adult's hand instead.

2. Mark the finger joints on the cut-out hand and fold the fingers at the lines.

3. Use scissors to cut out three wedges from each straw, lining the cuts up with the joints in your cardboard hand. Make sure you don't cut all the way through!

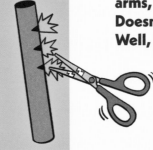

4. Tape the straws in place, one straw on each cardboard finger.

5. Cut five pieces of wool, about twice as long as your hand, and tie a knot in the ends.

6. Starting from the fingertips, thread each piece of the wool through a straw.

7. Now you can control your hand by pulling on the wool to move the fingers!

SMARTY PANTS!

Leonardo da Vinci designed a robot knight that could wave its arms, sit down and open its mouth. Doesn't sound too impressive? Well, he did it over 500 years ago!

IT'S ALIVE!

SCAVENGER HUNT

Can you **find all these items** in your garden or neighbourhood? You can do this **on your own** or **with a friend**.

Try to **think outside the box** – the more unusual the item, the more points you'll get!

FIND SOMETHING ...

1. that makes a noise

2. you can chew

3. with wheels

4. you can bend

A PEN (1 point)
A CHALKY ROCK (2 points)

5. you can write with

6. that smells weird

7. that a pirate might use

8. that is crooked

9. that is yellow and see-through

10. that tastes sweet

11. with the letter Q in it

12. with a face

13. that will grow

22.

that you'd use in outer space

23.

that is older than you

21.

that looks like something else

20.

that floats in water

24.

in a different language

19.

that you can wear

18.

that is magnetic

A FRIDGE MAGNET
(1 point)

A CREDIT CARD
(2 points)

25.

that is your favourite colour

Scavenger Hunt
This Way

17.

that starts with the first letter of your name

When you've found as many as you can, count up your score. You might need a judge to help you decide the points – no cheating!

1 POINT
– something easy

2 POINTS
– something strange

16.

the shape of a star

15.

with hair

A DOLL (1 point)

AN OLD POTATO
(2 points)

14.

that is sticky

YOUR SCORE:

GARDEN OLYMPICS

2 1 3

Team Ireland performed brilliantly in the **Tokyo Olympics**. Kellie Harrington, Paul O'Donovan and Fintan McCarthy took home gold medals, and Aifric Keogh, Eimear Lambe, Fiona Murtagh, Emily Hegarty and Aidan Walsh won bronze.

Try these events with your friends to see who'll be joining the Irish team in Paris 2024!

SPORTY SCRAMBLE

Can you unscramble the names of these Olympic sports? HINT: Team Ireland won medals in some of these events this year!

GMYCSSNITA

WGIMMSNI

NAKGTSI

XBGONI

SIGKNI

RWGONI

EVENT 1:

CRAZY BALANCE BEAM
Lay a long hosepipe out on the ground in a wiggly shape. Add in a couple of loops to make it more difficult. Each Olympian has to walk from one end of the hose to the other without falling off. The fastest wins!

EVENT 2:

WATER BALLOON SHOT PUT
Mark a start line and fill a water balloon for each Olympian. Start by facing backwards, then spin around and throw it! See who can throw their balloon the farthest.

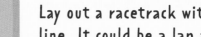

EVENT 3:

LONG JUMP

You'll need a long, straight patch of grass for this one. Lay out a pile of cushions at the end of your track. Mark the start line with a piece of string. Run up to the line and jump. Who can jump the farthest?

EVENT 4:

TUG OF WAR

You'll need at least two people, one on each side of the rope. If you have more than that, try to balance out the teams so that they are fair – one adult equals two children! Get a long, thick piece of rope and tie a knot in the middle. Make two lines on the grass and lay the rope out with the knot in the middle. The first team to pull the knot over their line wins.

EVENT 5:

SKIPPING ROPE RACE

Lay out a racetrack with a starting line. It could be a lap around the garden, or as far as a tree and back. Each Olympian gets a skipping rope (or you could take turns). When the race starts, you have to skip rope all the way around the track. If you take a step without skipping, you have to go back to the start. The fastest wins!

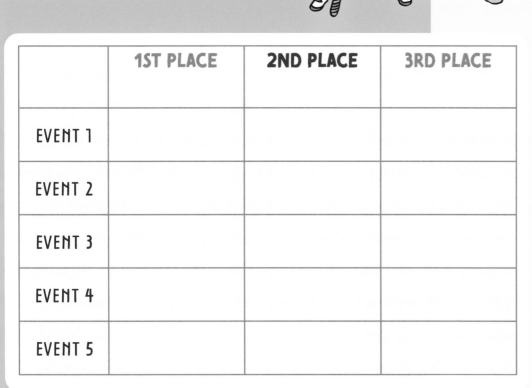

SMARTY PANTS!

In ancient Greece, Olympic athletes didn't worry about having fancy runners or the best gear. Often, they did sporting events completely naked ... it's a good thing Greece is a lot warmer than Ireland!

	1ST PLACE	2ND PLACE	3RD PLACE
EVENT 1			
EVENT 2			
EVENT 3			
EVENT 4			
EVENT 5			

SPY GAMES

Can you become a **secret agent** and fill in your top-secret fact file? **For your eyes only ...**

FIRST THINGS FIRST – YOU CAN'T USE YOUR REAL NAME IF YOU'RE GOING TO BE A SECRET AGENT.

Create a codename using the month you were born and the first letter of your name.

MONTH	FIRST NAME
JANUARY	Frozen
FEBRUARY	Flower
MARCH	Speedy
APRIL	Silver
MAY	Scarlet
JUNE	Diamond
JULY	Golden
AUGUST	Rogue
SEPTEMBER	Poison
OCTOBER	Steel
NOVEMBER	Dark
DECEMBER	Midnight

LETTER	SECOND NAME
A	Ninja
B	Eagle
C	Fox
D	Shadow
E	Hunter
F	Warrior
G	Thunder
H	Flash
I	Archer
J	Viper
K	Wolf
L	Lightning
M	Rider
N	Phantom
O	Warder
P	Knight
Q	Beast
R	Phoenix
S	Fang
T	Wind
U	Dragon
V	Storm
W	Ghost
X	Hornet
Y	Runner
Z	Feather

THE CASE OF THE MISSING DIAMOND

THE CASE OF THE PHANTOM FARTER

NEXT, DECIDE ON YOUR CURRENT MISSION.

_____

_____

THE CASE OF THE ROLLERBLADING VAMPIRE

NOW, THINK OF SOME EQUIPMENT YOU MIGHT BRING ON THAT MISSION.

_____

_____

_____

INVISIBLE INK
ROLLERBLADE
WHOOPEE CUSHION

FINALLY, MAKE A RECORD OF YOUR FINGERPRINT.

You'll need a piece of sandpaper, a graphite pencil (4B or 6B), sticky tape and some white paper.

1. Scribble on a piece of sandpaper with the soft pencil until you get some dark powder.

2. Dip your finger into the powder, then shake off any extra.

3. Place the tape sticky-side up and press your fingertip down firmly.

4. Flip the tape over and stick it in your fact file.

SECRET AGENT FACT FILE

TOP SECRET

CODENAME:

_____

AGE: _____   **HEIGHT:** _____

EYE COLOUR: _____

FINGERPRINT:

RUGBY RUMBLE

CAN YOU MAKE IT ALL THE WAY TO THE CUP?

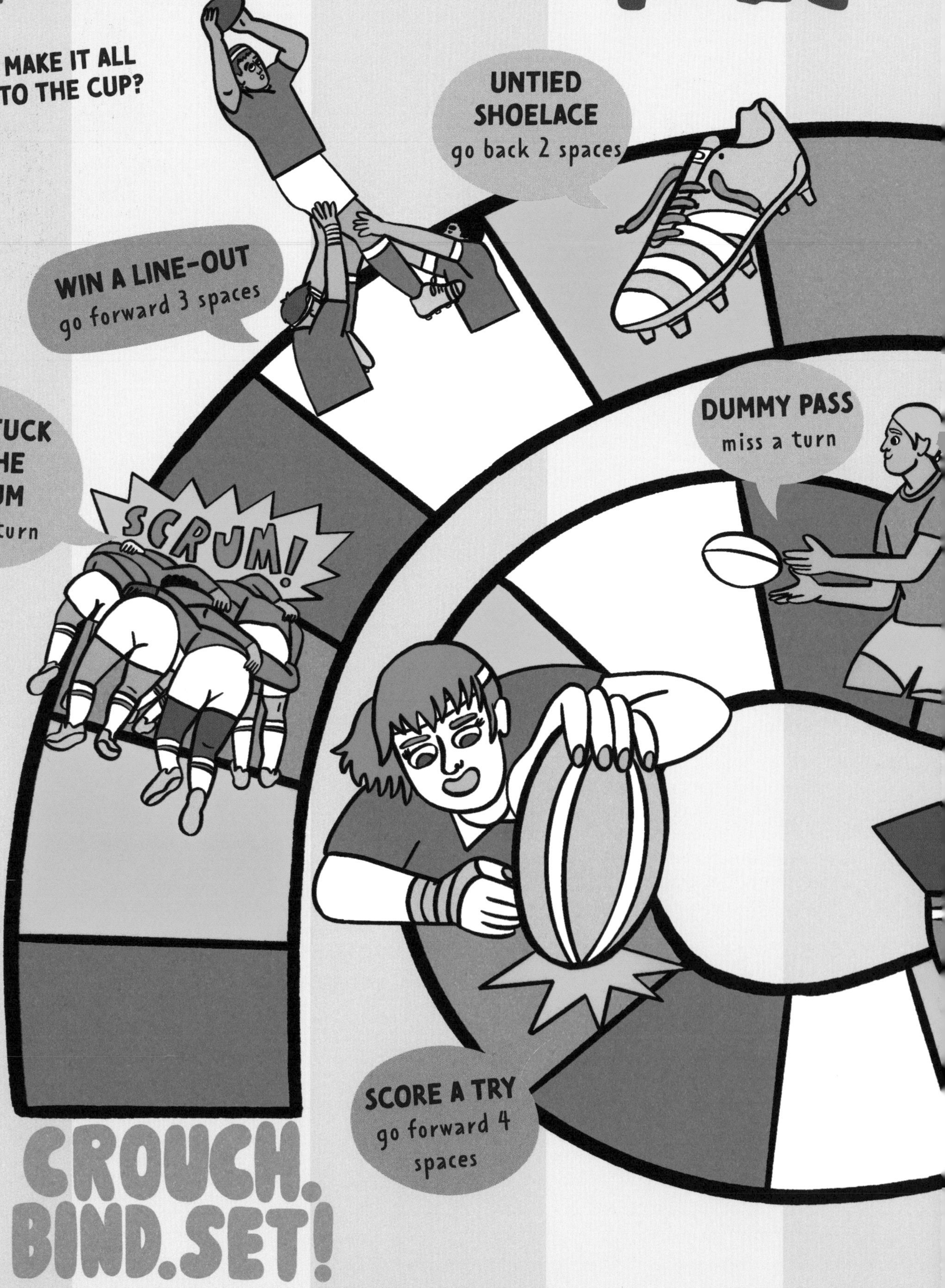

You'll need a **dice** and something to represent your player, like a **coin**.

WIN!

RED CARD
go back to the start

SCORE A CONVERSION
go forward 2 spaces

TACKLE
slide backwards 1 space

DROP GOAL
go forward 3 spaces

REF'S CAUTION
miss a turn

FREE KICK
fly forward 4 spaces

KITCHEN CORNER

ARE YOU A MASTER CHEF OR CAN YOU BURN A GLASS OF WATER? BON APPETIT ...

THIS BANANA NICE-CREAM MAKES ENOUGH FOR FOUR.

NICE CREAM, YOU SCREAM

4 overripe bananas

100ml of your favourite milk

Flavourings*

1. Peel and chop the bananas into chunks. Put them into a freezer bag and freeze overnight.

2. When the bananas are completely hard, put them in a food processor with the milk and blitz until it all turns creamy and soft.

3. Return to the freezer for at least an hour.

*Try these flavour ideas:

Berry – add 100g frozen raspberries before you blend.

Minty – add 2 drops of peppermint extract before you blend.

Nutty – once blended, swirl through 4 tbsp nut butter.

Choc-chip – once blended, stir in 50g chocolate chips.

WHICH IS YOUR FAVOURITE? DO YOU HAVE ANY OTHER FLAVOUR IDEAS?

MASH   BOIL

CHOP   SQUEEZE

SLICE   GRATE

STIR   WHISK

PEEL   BEAT

I	O	T	S	Y	T	S	H	X	E	W	V	N	P	L
N	U	X	E	V	T	Q	L	S	U	B	B	I	B	J
S	Q	U	E	E	Z	E	L	I	A	P	H	Z	S	C
U	G	N	E	N	S	T	I	I	C	M	I	T	U	I
P	C	H	C	W	G	J	O	M	M	E	I	A	G	A
K	S	I	H	W	R	T	B	Q	R	R	F	E	Q	Y
R	Q	P	I	K	A	Z	S	H	L	S	B	B	P	N
Y	W	V	J	L	T	N	D	G	O	T	Z	R	P	R
V	U	N	B	B	E	I	M	L	C	I	K	I	C	U
U	Y	Q	Y	K	F	H	I	H	E	J	O	I	S	E
B	M	J	M	F	B	T	T	I	Y	E	Z	F	P	U
L	C	T	K	R	C	A	W	L	Y	P	P	P	P	N
O	J	E	N	H	F	A	H	B	G	P	G	O	F	G
H	O	X	H	U	X	M	N	F	T	E	H	N	A	S
J	G	S	D	W	D	W	M	V	K	C	B	Q	Y	C

TRUE OR FALSE?

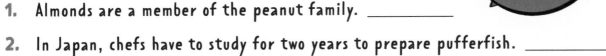

1. Almonds are a member of the peanut family. _____

2. In Japan, chefs have to study for two years to prepare pufferfish. _____

3. Pizza Margherita was named after a queen. _____

4. Coffee was used as money by the ancient Mayans. _____

5. Consecotaleophobia is a fear of chopsticks. _____

6. Potatoes are 10% water. _____

7. The most expensive cheese in the world is made from donkey's milk. _____

8. An astronaut once smuggled a sandwich on board a trip to space. _____

9. The burger was named after Lord Burger. _____

10. Pistachio nuts are flammable and can even spontaneously combust. _____

THE GREAT BIG

Are you a **Lego master** or a bit of a blockhead? Try these **30 challenges** and find out.

CAN YOU BUILD...

Day 1.

SOMETHING USING EXACTLY 50 PIECES

Day 2.

A VOLCANO ERUPTING

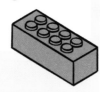

Day 3.

A WILD ANIMAL

Day 4.

A GAA PLAYER
(See page 12 for ideas!)

Day 5.

SOMETHING WITH YOUR EYES CLOSED

Day 6.

AN IMPOSSIBLE MACHINE

Day 7.

A SPACESHIP
(See page 48 for ideas!)

Day 8.

SOMETHING USING ONLY TWO COLOURS

Day 9.

THE TALLEST TOWER YOU CAN

Day 10.

A BRIDGE OVER SOMETHING

Day 11.

A MUSICAL INSTRUMENT
(See page 34 for ideas!)

Day 12.

A MEMBER OF YOUR FAMILY

Day 13.

AN ALIEN CREATURE

Day 14.

A TV CHARACTER

Day 15.

AN IRISH LANDMARK

LEGO CHALLENGE

Day 16.
A NORMAN CASTLE

Day 17.
A SCENE FROM YOUR FAVOURITE MOVIE

Day 18.
A TWISTY, TURNY MAZE

Day 19.
A COLOURFUL IGLOO

Day 20.
A TERRIFYING MONSTER FACE

Day 21.
A GIANT PIZZA

Day 22.
THE GPO
(See page 36 for ideas!)

Day 23.
YOUR NAME OUT OF BRICKS

Day 24.
A BOAT THAT FLOATS

Day 25.
A PAIR OF UNDERPANTS

Day 26.
A PATTERN THAT REPEATS OVER AND OVER AGAIN

Day 27.
YOUR COUNTY'S FLAG

Day 28.
A GAME OF Xs AND Os

Day 29.
A RAINBOW

Day 30.
A MAP OF IRELAND
(See page 16 for help!)

CRAIC AGUS CEOL

IRELAND IS FAMOUS AROUND THE WORLD FOR OUR DANCE, OUR MUSIC AND OUR SENSE OF FUN.

Join the dots to discover the **INSTRUMENT**

TUNING UP

Musicians use **SHEET MUSIC** to tell them what to play next in a song. Each line and space on the **STAFF** is a different **NOTE**.

C D E F G A B C

Can you write the correct letter under each note in this piece of music? If you can, try to figure out the song!

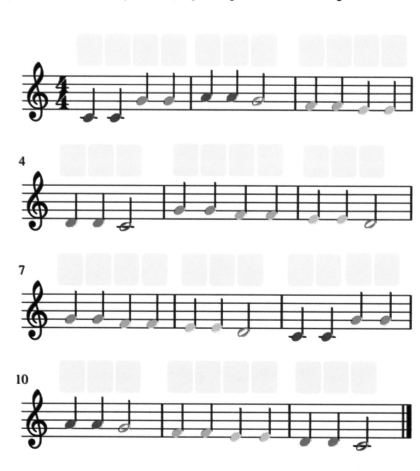

34

ACROSS

3. The national festival of Irish singing and dancing.

6. Cutlery that can be used to make music.

8. In the song, Molly Malone gathers _____ and mussels.

10. There is a statue of rocker _____ Lynott off Grafton St, Dublin.

11. Wild _____ is a traditional Irish folk song.

DOWN

1. Mundy released a song about this month.

2. Jigs and _____ are two popular types of Irish music.

4. The instrument that appears on the back of every Irish coin.

5. The lead singer of Irish band U2.

6. An Irish storyteller.

7. The Irish twins who represented Ireland twice in the Eurovision.

8. The Irish word for a group dance.

9. _____ O'Donnell is a singer popular with Irish mammies.

ALL SHOOK UP

Can you **unscramble** the names of these **seven instruments** that are **used to play Irish music**?

1. dlefid

2. tfuel

3. drabnoh

4. docronaci

5. int tsehiwl

6. nelnailu seppi

7. rhpa

THE GPO & 1916

The GPO is one of the most famous buildings in Ireland. Besides being the headquarters of An Post, it was also the site of the 1916 Easter Rising.

DiD YOU KNOW?

1

Dublin and **London** were in **different time zones** in 1916. Ireland followed Dublin Mean Time, which was **25 minutes behind**.

2

In 1916, mail was **delivered twice every day** in Dublin.

3

Constance Markievicz, an officer in the Irish Citizen Army, wrote a battle song for the Rising.

STAMP OF APPROVAL

An Post releases special stamps each year, celebrating Irish history, people and nature. Can you design a new stamp for 2022? Above are some ex**STAMP**les to get you started.

4

The Proclamation of Independence was printed in a hurry, so there were **lots of small mistakes.**

5

The British officer who took the **surrender of Rising leader Pádraig Pearse** went on to become a **Hollywood actor.**

6

One of the Volunteers, **Michael Walker**, had competed for Ireland on the **Olympic cycling team** in Stockholm in 1912.

7

The fighting was paused every day so that the **ducks** in St Stephen's Green **could be fed.**

8

Joseph Plunkett **married his fiancée**, Grace Gifford, at **Kilmainham Gaol** eight hours before his execution.

9

There were **1,784 people arrested** in Dublin in connection with the Easter Rising.

10

Badly **damaged by fire** during the Rising, the GPO did not **reopen until 1929.**

CRACK THE CODE

Can you unscramble this urgent message from Dublin 1916?

ELEAPS NOTD GTEROF

OT FDEE HET KDCUS

NI HTESSNPE ENEGR!

_____

_____

_____

URGENT

KEEPING FIT

Super coach **Brian Keane** is here with some tips to keep you moving and fighting fit. Brian is a fitness expert, trainer and coach. His favourite activity is football, and, in 2018, **he ran with the camels across the Sahara Desert!**

BRIAN SAYS: Why not set up your own obstacle course, just like in *Ireland's Fittest Family*? With a few simple items, you can have a go in your home, park or school playground.

3.

RUN ACROSS A BALANCE BEAM

START

2.

HOP IN A SACK

1.

FROG LEAP BETWEEN CONES

☀ **BRIAN'S TOP TIPS**

Use your bodyweight to improve your strength. I started doing push-ups, stomach crunches and pull-ups in my bedroom when I was 11. My daughter Holly (6) does pull-ups on the monke bars. You're never too young to start!

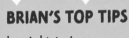

5.
CRAWL UNDER
A BLANKET

BRIAN'S TOP TIPS

The secret to motivation is to find something you enjoy. If you don't like team sports, you could join a club for karate, swimming, gymnastics or ballet.

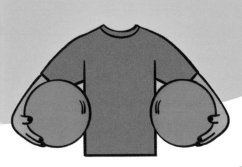

6.
SPRINT TO THE
FINISH LINE

4.
CARRY A BALL
UNDER EACH ARM

When you've finished, sit down with some **NICE-CREAM** (page 30) and draw yourself and your fellow racers on this podium.

2   **1**   **3**

AROUND THE WORLD

The Seven Wonders of the New World are **INCREDIBLE** buildings made by many different civilizations over the years. Which ones are on your **BUCKET LIST**?

Taj Mahal, India, AD 1643
A marble palace built by an emperor in memory of his wife.

Machu Picchu, Peru, AD 1450
An Incan city in the clouds, 2,500 metres above sea level.

The Great Wall, China, 700 BC
A stone wall that covers over 20,000 km of China.

Chichen Itza, Mexico, AD 600
A Mayan temple built to honour an ancient snake god.

Christ the Redeemer, Brazil, AD 1931
A 38-metre-tall statue that towers over the city of Rio.

Petra, Jordan, 312 BC
An ancient city carved out of sandstone in the desert.

The Colosseum, Italy, AD 80
A 50,000-seat stadium built by the Romans.

BUCKET LIST

BUILD THE BEST

Are you up to the task?
Can you design the **EIGHTH WONDER OF THE WORLD**?

Mine is made entirely out of cheese!

My wonder is smaller than a grain of rice.

ROLL UP, ROLL UP!

★ ★ ★ ★ ★ ★ ★

◆ WELCOME TO THE GRAND OPENING OF THE EIGHTH WONDER OF THE WORLD:

_____

PREPARE TO BE AMAZED, ASTONISHED AND ASTOUNDED!

Mine has slides coming from every window.

SMARTY PANTS!

The original Seven Wonders of the Ancient World have all been lost over the years ... except one, the Great Pyramid of Giza, which is still standing strong in Egypt!

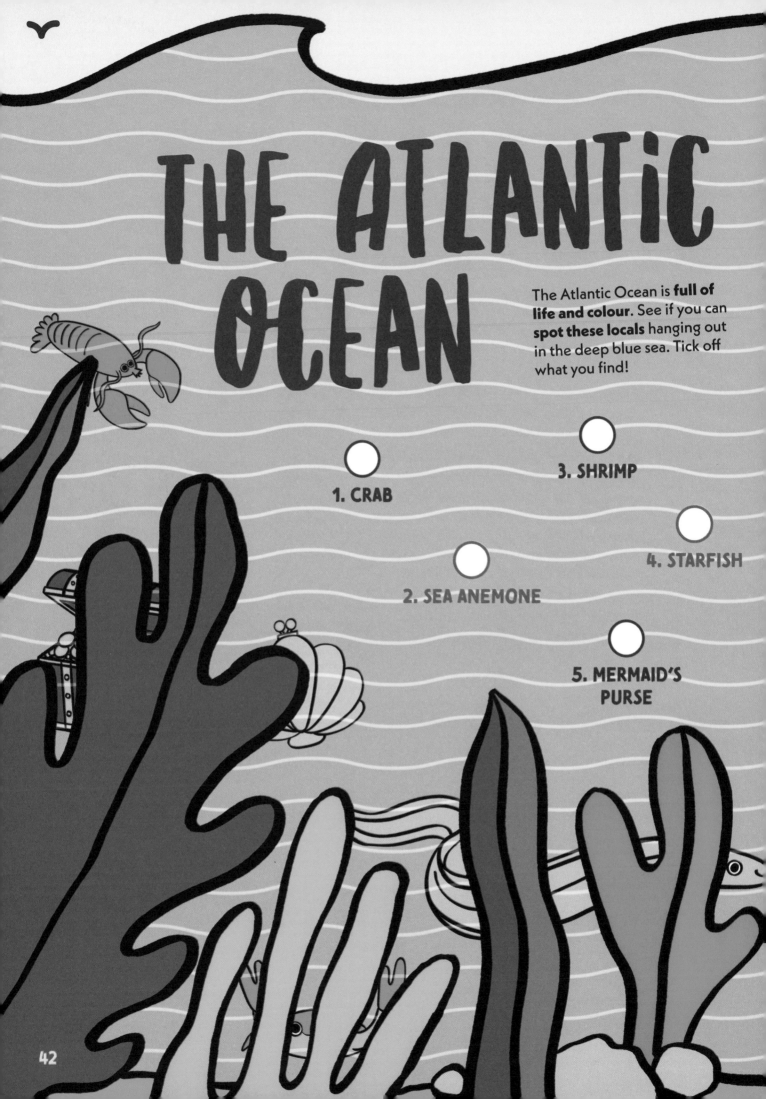

THE ATLANTIC OCEAN

The Atlantic Ocean is **full of life and colour**. See if you can **spot these locals** hanging out in the deep blue sea. Tick off what you find!

1. CRAB

2. SEA ANEMONE

3. SHRIMP

4. STARFISH

5. MERMAID'S PURSE

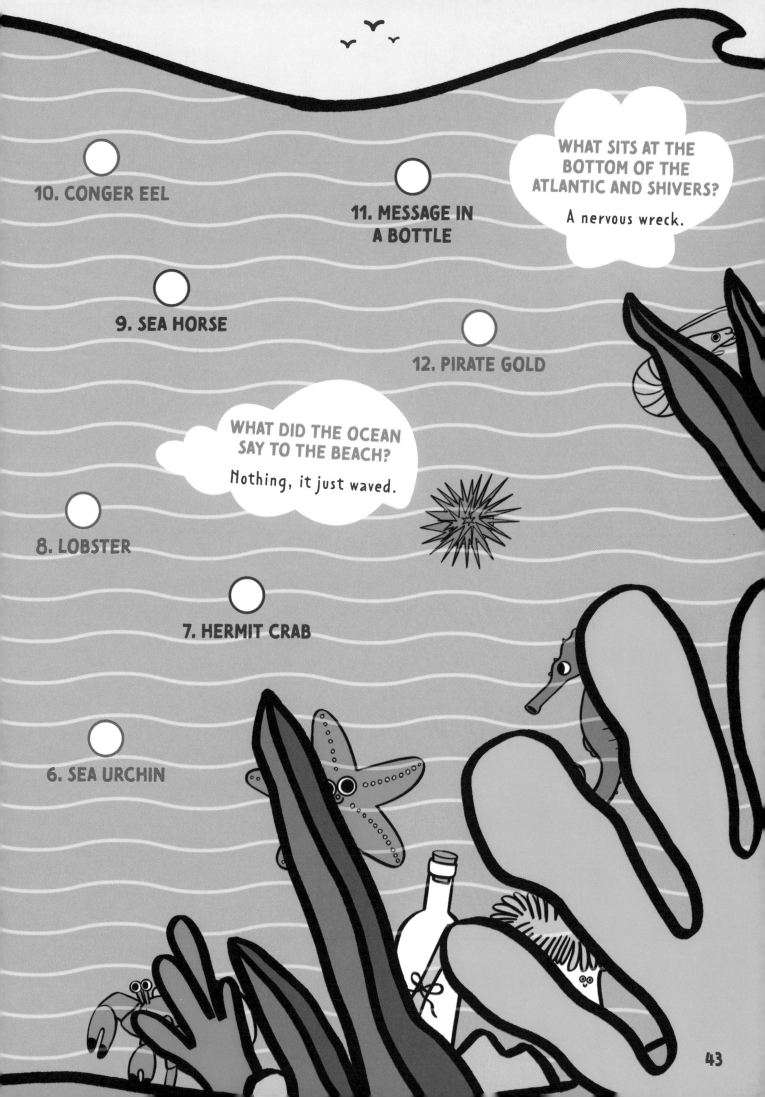

10. CONGER EEL

11. MESSAGE IN A BOTTLE

WHAT SITS AT THE BOTTOM OF THE ATLANTIC AND SHIVERS?

A nervous wreck.

9. SEA HORSE

12. PIRATE GOLD

WHAT DID THE OCEAN SAY TO THE BEACH?

Nothing, it just waved.

8. LOBSTER

7. HERMIT CRAB

6. SEA URCHIN

HAUNTING HALLOWEEN

MONSTER MASH-UP

DID YOU KNOW THAT THE CELTS INVENTED HALLOWEEN?

During the ancient festival of Samhain, the Celts would light fires and wear costumes to scare away ghosts.

ARGH!

4

3

Can you come up with the **scariest monster EVER**? You'll need a friend, sibling or parent to help you out.

2

1. First, draw the legs of your monster in Box 1. Then cover it with a piece of paper. No peeking!

2. Your friend draws the monster's waist in Box 2, then covers the first two boxes.

3. You draw the chest and arms in Box 3, cover the first three boxes, and then hand it back.

4. Your friend fills in the head in Box 4.

5. Lift the piece of paper to reveal your Monster Mash-up!

1

OMG!

PUKING PUMPKIN

What was your HALLOWEEN OUTFIT THIS YEAR?

_____

What do you plan to dress up as NEXT YEAR?

_____

This Halloween, make sure your house looks absolutely **DISGUSTING** with this dreadful decoration.

1. First, cut a hole in the top of your pumpkin and scoop out all the slimy, seedy insides. Put them aside in a bowl.

2. Draw your pumpkin's face using a marker. Give it scrunched-up eyes and a mouth – make it nice and big!

3. Ask an adult to help carve out the face using a sharp knife.

4. Put your pumpkin somewhere visible, like your front step.

5. Arrange the slimy insides so it looks like they are pouring out of the pumpkin's mouth. Get ready to send trick or treaters running!

Check out this word search for some monstrous ideas!

O	M	S	L	I	A	T	E	D	K	B	U	S	G	W
J	G	Q	E	M	D	X	U	J	G	W	L	U	O	L
L	R	U	F	L	V	B	F	Z	I	K	M	A	S	K
A	S	U	I	N	A	I	E	N	P	E	S	J	W	E
S	H	O	O	F	S	C	G	G	K	F	J	C	V	N
C	R	F	S	G	Q	S	S	X	E	L	B	P	O	W
Z	U	M	G	Q	J	U	H	S	L	I	U	I	V	E
P	I	J	N	D	M	S	B	B	X	Y	N	N	U	H
E	O	B	A	D	N	N	S	Q	Q	O	P	V	N	Q
X	M	I	F	V	D	N	C	T	A	F	T	Y	H	M
F	L	I	S	O	R	D	L	S	H	Q	C	F	F	L
B	H	N	L	O	C	N	A	B	M	E	P	T	O	X
Y	N	X	H	S	N	B	W	J	W	Q	W	V	U	Q
O	U	R	M	T	Y	W	S	N	I	T	N	B	K	U
N	U	U	M	C	F	T	U	S	Z	B	J	Y	C	D

CLAWS	**HORNS**
HOOFS	**SLIME**
SCALES	**FUR**
WINGS	**POISON**
FANGS	**TAIL**

SOCCER SHOWDOWN

In 2021, fans around the world were glued to the Euros. Italy beat England in a thrilling penalty shoot-out.

Now, get ready for the **2022 WORLD CUP IN QATAR** with these play-offs!

TACKLE TEST

Can you spot the **5 differences** between these two pictures?

Only two goalkeepers have ever captained Republic of Ireland soccer teams – Alan Kelly and Shay Given.

OPEN GOAL

It's extra time in the World Cup final, and you have the ball. Can you dribble it past the other players and beat the goalie?

THE BOOT-iFUL GAME

What does the colour of your boots say about you?

- **RED** - a risk-taker
- **BLUE** - a smooth striker
- **GREEN** - a cool defender
- **YELLOW** - a real speed machine
- **ORANGE** - loves a trick shot
- **PURPLE** - slick and stylish footwork
- **BLACK** - an old pro
- **WHITE** - a real chancer

Mix and match these colours to design your very own pair of soccer boots!

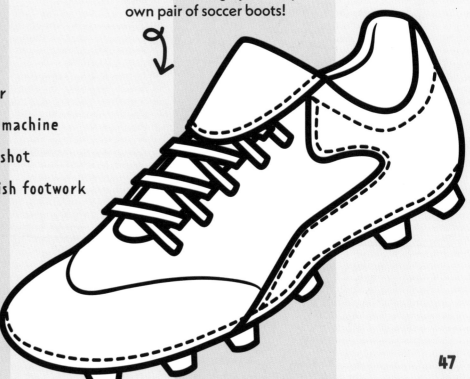

47

OUTER SPACE

WHETHER IT'S ONE SMALL STEP OR AN EPIC LUNAR BLAST-OFF, YOU CAN ROCKET PAST THE FINAL FRONTIER!

WRITTEN IN THE STARS

How many of these constellations can you spot in the night sky? Match the names to the pictures and colour them in.

URSA MAJOR

ORION

SIRIUS

LEO

CYGNUS

CASSIOPEIA

PEGASUS

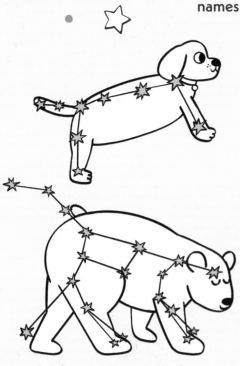

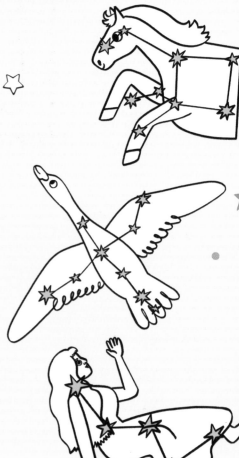

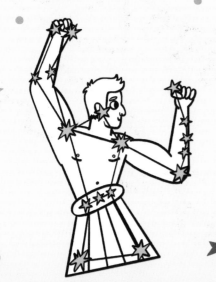

Tip: It will take your eyes about 15 minutes to adjust to the darkness. Why not drink some yummy hot chocolate while you wait?

BLACK HOLE FUN

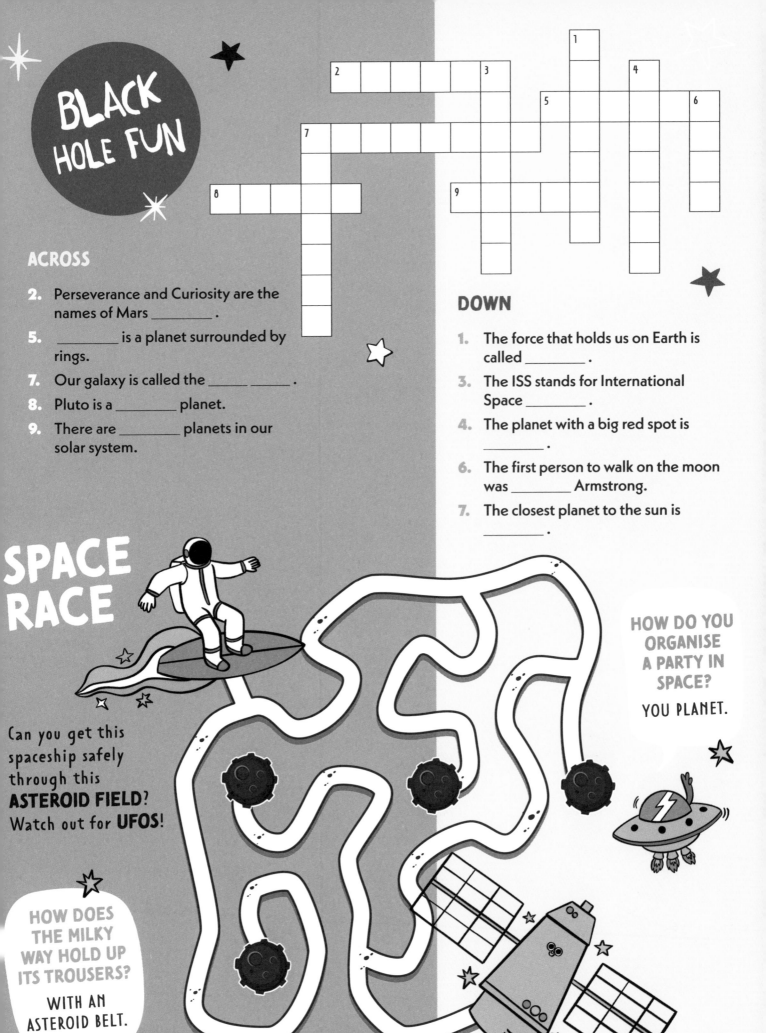

ACROSS

2. Perseverance and Curiosity are the names of Mars _____ .
5. _____ is a planet surrounded by rings.
7. Our galaxy is called the _____ _____ .
8. Pluto is a _____ planet.
9. There are _____ planets in our solar system.

DOWN

1. The force that holds us on Earth is called _____ .
3. The ISS stands for International Space _____ .
4. The planet with a big red spot is _____ .
6. The first person to walk on the moon was _____ Armstrong.
7. The closest planet to the sun is _____ .

SPACE RACE

Can you get this spaceship safely through this **ASTEROID FIELD**? Watch out for **UFOS**!

HOW DO YOU ORGANISE A PARTY IN SPACE?

YOU PLANET.

HOW DOES THE MILKY WAY HOLD UP ITS TROUSERS?

WITH AN ASTEROID BELT.

49

NEWGRANGE

Newgrange is a **Stone Age passage tomb** in Co. Meath that is over **5,000 years old.**

On the **shortest day of the year**, the winter solstice, something amazing happens.

The rising sun lines up with the doorway and **lights up the passage tomb.**

stylish stones

MANY ROCKS AROUND NEWGRANGE ARE COVERED WITH LINES, LOZENGES, AND TRIPLE SPIRAL SYMBOLS CALLED **TRISKELES**.

Can you decorate this standing stone with the same design?

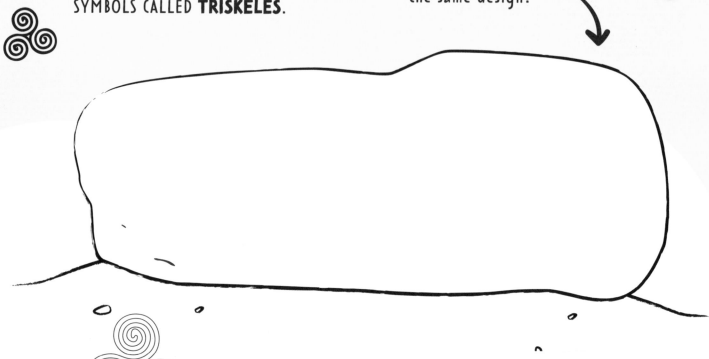

TEXTING THROUGH TIME

Can you use this **ANCIENT CODE** to translate a message left by the Newgrange builders?

Once you've figured it out, you can use this code to write your own secret messages!

A	B	C
D	E	F
G	H	I

J•	K••	L•
M•	N••	•O
•P	•Q•	R•

```
     S
T  X  U
     V
```

```
     W
X •••• Y
     Z
```

SMARTY PANTS!

Newgrange is 500 years older than the Pyramids of Giza in Egypt, and 1,000 years older than Stonehenge in England!

TOY SHOW TIME

It's that time of year – time to stick on your pyjamas, stay up way past your bedtime and watch *The Late Late Toy Show*!

Every year, **RYAN TUBRIDY** wears lots of different Christmas jumpers as he hosts the Toy Show. **CAN YOU COLOUR IN THIS ONE FOR HIM?**

Tip: Make it as colourful and Christmassy as you can!

WHAT'S ON YOUR TOY SHOW WISH LIST?

1

2

3

TALK TO THE HAND

Sign language is a way of communicating using your hands.

The Late Late Toy Show has an **Irish Sign Language interpreter**, so people who are hard of hearing can enjoy the show. Learn how to spell your name with the **ISL alphabet!**

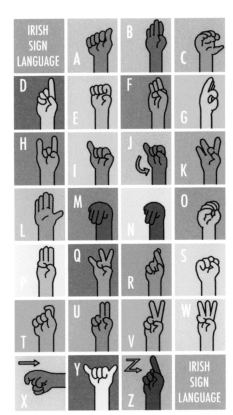

© Ray Watson

SNACK ATTACK

Why not rustle up some crunchy toffee popcorn to snack on while you watch *The Late Late Toy Show?*

1 tbsp sunflower oil
2 tbsp popcorn kernels
20g butter
pinch of salt
20g brown sugar
1 tbsp golden syrup

1. Put the oil in a big saucepan on a medium heat.

2. Tip in the popcorn and swirl the kernels around in the oil.

3. Put the lid on, then turn the heat down to low. Listen for popping! As soon as the popping stops, take the saucepan off the heat.

4. Melt the butter in a separate saucepan with the salt, brown sugar and golden syrup. Stir on a high heat for two minutes.

5. Pour the toffee over the popped popcorn, put the lid on the pan and shake to mix the toffee sauce.

6. Tip the toffee popcorn into a bowl and let it cool, breaking up any chunks as you wait.

IT'S FINALLY HERE!

CHRISTMAS

Santa Pause

It's the day after Christmas and Santa is on his day off. Colour him in – Let's hope he put on sun cream!

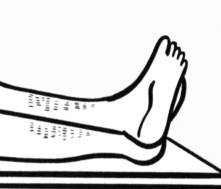

SMARTY PANTS!

The first artificial Christmas trees weren't trees at all ... They were made out of goose feathers dyed green!

TAKE THE REINS

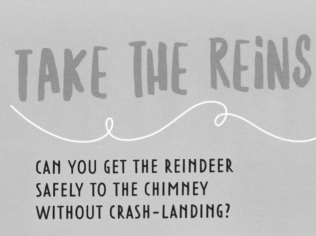

CAN YOU GET THE REINDEER
SAFELY TO THE CHIMNEY
WITHOUT CRASH-LANDING?

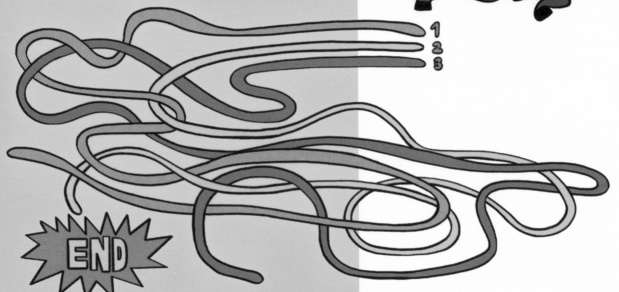

1
2
3

END

TREE-MENDOUS

Can you match the
Christmas tree
with its shadow?

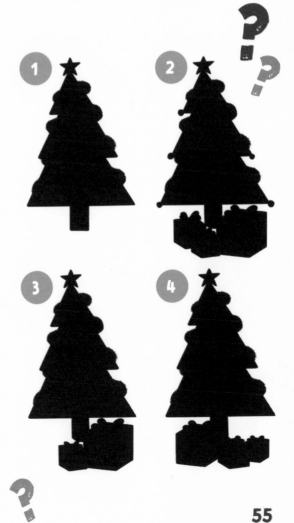

1

2

3

4

55

BiG QUiZ

How's your general knowledge? Were you paying attention this year? It's time to get quizzical ...

ROUND 1

1. What is a baby elephant called?

2. How many sides does a hexagon have?

3. What is the name of Michael D. Higgins' new dog?

4. Who became president of the United States in 2021?

5. Tayto Park is in which county?

6. What famous ship sank after it left Cork in 1912?

7. What is the slowest mammal in the world?

8. What medal did Kellie Harrington win in the Tokyo Olympics?

9. What was Minecraft originally called?

10. What is the official language of Brazil?

ROUND 2

1. What is the main ingredient of guacamole?

2. What colour are a ladybird's spots?

3. Which planet is closest to the sun?

4. What Disney movie, set in Italy, was released in 2021?

5. In what sport can you get a hole in one?

6. Stratus, cirrus, cumulus and nimbus are types of what?

7. What is the name of Ron Weasley's rat?

8. What do you call a scientist who studies rocks?

9. In what county would you find the Burren?

10. Which soccer team won the 2021 Euros?

OF 2021!

ROUND 3

1. What invisible line runs around the centre of the Earth?
2. What was the name of the Pirate Queen from Mayo?
3. Where will the Olympics take place in 2024?
4. What is the orange part of an egg called?
5. How many players are on a hurling team?
6. What is an alicorn?
7. What is the national plant of Scotland?
8. What connects a bull, horse, stag, salmon and harp?
9. On which island nation would you find lemurs?
10. In March 2021, a container ship got stuck in which canal?

ROUND 4

1. Who was the first man to walk on the moon?
2. What animal has a beak, fur, venomous spurs and lays eggs?
3. Who was Ireland's first female president?
4. What does the chemical symbol NaCl mean?
5. What country won the Eurovision in 2021?
6. What river flows through Cork?
7. What is the fastest animal in the world?
8. In the video game, what type of animal is Sonic?
9. What does KO stand for in fighting sports?
10. What telescope is NASA launching in 2021?

ANSWERS

PAGE 4

The missing number is 78.

PAGE 8

A. **TRUE!** Flower power!

B. **FALSE!** It's called a boar.

C. **TRUE!** It sounds pretty scary.

D. **TRUE!** A herd can be found in Killarney.

E. **FALSE!** They're shaped like helicopters.

F. **TRUE!** And they won't shut up about it!

G. **TRUE!** I wonder if they like to argue.

H. **FALSE!** The common lizard is native to Ireland.

I. **TRUE!** I hope they have good dentists.

J. **TRUE!** They report where the flowers are.

PAGE 12

PAGE 19

LADYBIRD = bóín dé (god's little cow)

JELLYFISH = smugairle róin (seal spit)

WOLF = mac tíre (son of the land)

FOX = madra rua (red dog)

BAT = sciathán leathair (leather wings)

PINE MARTEN = cat crainn (tree cat)

PORPOISE = muc mhara (pig of the sea)

DADDY LONGLEGS = snáthaid an phúca (the devil's needle)

PAGE 24

Gymnastics
Swimming
Skating
Boxing
Skiing
Rowing

PAGE 31

1. **FALSE!** They are a member of the rose family.

2. **TRUE!** The fish is very toxic.

3. **TRUE!** Queen Margherita of Italy.

4. **FALSE!** They used chocolate.

5. **TRUE!** Better keep a fork handy.

6. **FALSE!** They are 80% water.

7. **TRUE!** It is made in Serbia.

8. **TRUE!** A corned beef sandwich.

9. **FALSE!** But the sandwich was named after Lord Sandwich.

10. **TRUE!** So mind your lunchbox doesn't explode.

PAGE 34

THE SONG IS TWINKLE TWINKLE LITTLE STAR.

PAGE 35

ACROSS
3. Fleadh
6. Spoons
8. Cockles
10. Phil
11. Rover

DOWN
1. July
2. Reels
4. Harp
5. Bono
6. Seanchaí
7. Jedward
8. Ceili
9. Daniel

1. Fiddle
2. Flute
3. Bodhran
4. Accordion
5. Tin whistle
6. Uilleann pipes
7. Harp

PAGE 37

PLEASE DON'T FORGET TO FEED THE DUCKS IN STEPHEN'S GREEN!

PAGE 46

PAGE 49

ACROSS
2. Rovers
5. Saturn
7. Milky Way
8. Dwarf
9. Eight

DOWN
1. Gravity
3. Station
4. Jupiter
6. Neil
7. Mercury

PAGE 51

DON'T FORGET TO TURN OFF THE LIGHT

PAGE 56-57

ROUND 1
1. Calf
2. Six
3. Misneach
4. Joe Biden
5. Meath
6. Titanic
7. Sloth
8. Gold
9. Cave game
10. Portuguese

ROUND 2
1. Avocado
2. Black
3. Mercury
4. Luca
5. Golf
6. Cloud
7. Scabbers
8. Geologist
9. Clare
10. Italy

ROUND 3
1. Equator
2. Grace O'Malley, or Granuaile
3. Paris
4. Yolk
5. Fifteen
6. A unicorn horn
7. Thistle
8. They all appeared on Irish coins
9. Madagascar
10. Suez

ROUND 4
1. Neil Armstrong
2. Platypus
3. Mary Robinson
4. Salt
5. Italy
6. Lee
7. Cheetah
8. Hedgehog
9. Knockout
10. James Webb

Gill Books
Hume Avenue
Park West
Dublin 12
www.gillbooks.ie

Gill Books is an imprint of M.H. Gill and Co.

© Gill Books 2021

978 0717 1 9224 3

Text by Sheila Armstrong
Designed by grahamthew.com
Print origination by Sarah McCoy
Illustrations by Jacky Sheridan
Proofread by Jennifer Armstrong
Printed by Hussar Books, Poland

For permission to reproduce photographs, the author and publisher gratefully acknowledge the following:

© Alamy: 2, 12, 36, 37; © DSPCA: 18, 19; © Brendan Moran/Sportsfile via Getty Images: 24; © Brian Keane: 38; © Freepik: 1, 7, 8, 9, 18, 19, 20, 22, 24, 25, 26, 30, 31, 38, 39, 41, 44, 47, 51; © Getty images: 2; © iStock/Getty Premium: 2, 3, 4, 5, 6, 9, 11, 22, 23, 24, 25, 31, 32, 33, 33, 34, 36, 37, 40, 45, 48, 50, 53; © Maja Hitij/Getty Images: 24 ; © Peter Donnolly: 14; © Ray Watson: 52; © RTÉ: 52; © Shutterstock Premier: 13, 45, 46; © Wikimedia Commons: 3, 21, 36, 38, 40.

This book is typeset in Neue Kabel and Tomarik.

The paper used in this book comes from the wood pulp of managed forests. For every tree felled, at least one tree is planted, thereby renewing natural resources.

5 4 3 2 1

THANKS FOR THE HELP!
Peter Donnelly
Gillian at the DSPCA
Brian Keane (and Holly!)
3rd Class Canal Way ETNS 2020/21
Nicky, Cleo, Stella, Laura and Kate